Dear Parent:

Congratulations! Your child is taking the first steps on an exciting journey. The destination? Independent reading!

STEP INTO READING® will help your child get there. The program offers five steps to reading success. Each step includes fun stories and colorful art. There are also Step into Reading Sticker Books, Step into Reading Math Readers, Step into Reading Phonics Readers, Step into Reading Write-In Readers, and Step into Reading Phonics Boxed Sets—a complete literacy program with something for every child.

Learning to Read, Step by Step!

Ready to Read   Preschool–Kindergarten
• big type and easy words • rhyme and rhythm • picture clues
For children who know the alphabet and are eager to begin reading.

Reading with Help   Preschool–Grade 1
• basic vocabulary • short sentences • simple stories
For children who recognize familiar words and sound out new words with help.

Reading on Your Own   Grades 1–3
• engaging characters • easy-to-follow plots • popular topics
For children who are ready to read on their own.

Reading Paragraphs   Grades 2–3
• challenging vocabulary • short paragraphs • exciting stories
For newly independent readers who read simple sentences with confidence.

Ready for Chapters   Grades 2–4
• chapters • longer paragraphs • full-color art
For children who want to take the plunge into chapter books but still like colorful pictures.

STEP INTO READING® is designed to give every child a successful reading experience. The grade levels are only guides. Children can progress through the steps at their own speed, developing confidence in their reading, no matter what their grade.

Remember, a lifetime love of reading starts with a single step!

STORIES ABOUT BEES AND TREES AND FEET AND FUR— AND MORE!

Visit us on the Web!
StepIntoReading.com
Seussville.com
pbskids.org/catinthehat
treehousetv.com

Educators and librarians, for a variety of teaching tools, visit us at RHTeachersLibrarians.com

ISBN: 978-0-375-97304-8

Printed in the United States of America 10 9 8 7 6 5 4 3 2 1

First Edition

STEP INTO READING®

STORIES ABOUT BEES AND TREES AND FEET AND FUR— AND MORE!

Step 2 and 3 Books

A Collection of Five Early Readers

Random House 🏠 New York

Contents

Show Me the Honey 9

Step This Way 55

The Tree Doctor 85

Now You See Me 115

Hooray for Hair! 145

Show Me the Honey

by Tish Rabe

from a script by Ken Cuperus

illustrated by Christopher Moroney

Random House 🏠 New York

"This morning," said Nick,

"I'd like honey on toast.

That is the breakfast that

I like the most!"

"Me too," said Sally,

"but I'm sorry to say,

it looks like we're all

out of honey today."

"Sally," Nick said,
"your joke isn't funny.
I can't eat my breakfast
if we're out of honey!"

"Did someone say 'honey'?"
cried the Cat. "What a treat!
It's gloppy and sloppy
and sticky and sweet.
I love it on pancakes,
all fluffy and hot.
Please pour me a bit
of the honey you've got!"

"It's all gone," said Nick.

"Is there some in your hat?"

"Oh dear . . . ," said the Cat.

"No, I do not have that.

But I have something else—

a Special Invitation

to Queen Priscilla Buzzoo's

Dance-All-Day Celebration!

She is queen of the bees

and her parties are great.

But we've got to hurry

or we will be late!"

14

"There's one problem," said Sally.

"Look here and you'll see—

to go to the party

you must be a bee."

Queen Priscilla Buzzoo's
Dance-All-Day Celebration
Meet at the hive
at a quarter past five.
(Bees only, please.)

"Don't worry," the Cat said.

"I know what to do.

This is a job for

Thing One and Thing Two!"

So the two Things ran in and
the Cat asked them, "Please,
do something to make us
fit in with the bees."

In a flash those two Things,
with their usual knack,
striped the kids and the Cat
with yellow and black.

"I can't believe it," said Nick.

"I look just like a bee.

This is something that I

never thought I would see!"

"We're off!" said the Cat.

"We will meet Queen Buzzoo.

We'll meet her and greet her

and dance with her too!

Push the Shrinkamadoodle

if you would, please.

It will shrink us down to

the size of the bees."

"We'll fly past the ladybugs
and wave to the birds,
who will sing us some songs
that don't have any words.
We will soar and, what's more,
we will dip and we'll dive
through a hole in a tree
and down into the hive."

They got to the party
a few minutes late
and were stopped by two bees
who were guarding the gate.
"Excuse me," one said.
"Where is your invitation
to Queen Priscilla Buzzoo's
Dance-All-Day Celebration?"
"Here it is!" Sally said.
The bees said, "Go in!
The special bee dance
is about to begin!"

"Nick and Sally," the Cat said,
"let me introduce you
    to the queen of the bees,
    Queen Priscilla Buzzoo."
"Hello," said the queen.
"Welcome to my hive.
    My party just started
    at a quarter past five."
"Your Beeness," Nick said,
"I'd like to thank you.
    This is the first party
    of bees I've been to!"

Then they heard buzzing,
and in front of the throne
one worker bee started
to dance all alone!
She zigged and she zagged,
then she wiggled
and waggled.

She slipped and she slid
and she jiggled and jaggled.
She swirled and she twirled
with a buzz and a spin,
and then . . .

. . . more and more bees
began to join in!

Soon all the bees were
dancing and twirling.
Wings and antennae
were swinging and swirling.
Then Sally and Nick
began to dance too.
"Bee-utiful!" cried
Queen Priscilla Buzzoo.

"Watch the bees!" said the Cat.
"And you'll get a surprise—
they aren't just dancing
to get exercise!"

36

"The first bee that danced,"
Sally said, "let me guess.
She was showing them something."
The Cat cried out, "Yes!"

"Her dance showed something
bees need to survive—
where to find nectar to
bring to the hive.
They get nectar from flowers.
It's sticky and sweet.
They use it to make the
sweet honey they eat."

"Her special bee dance
lets the other bees know
where to find flowers
and which way to go."

"Can we help them?" asked Sally.

The Cat said, "Indeed!

We can follow and help them

find nectar they need."

"To the Thinga-ma-jigger!
Get ready to fly.
Hold on to your hats
and we'll take to the sky!"
"Let's go!" said Nick.
"If we hurry, we'll see
how bees make honey.
How hard could it be?"

So they flew with the bees
and slurped nectar from flowers,
then returned to the hive
in a couple of hours.

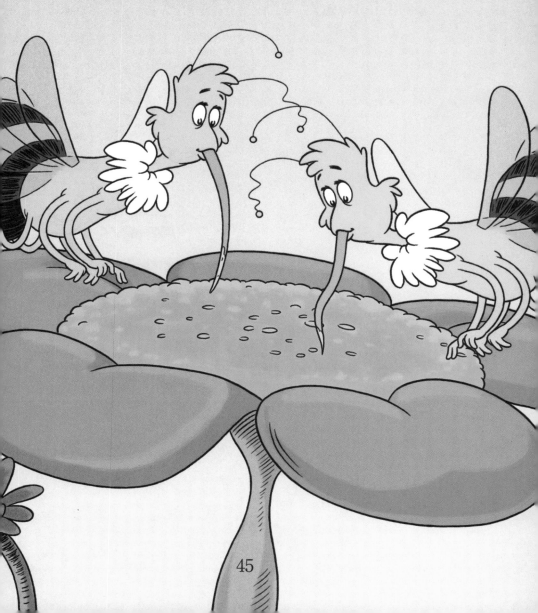

45

At the hive they spit nectar
into combs, where it dried.
Soon all of those combs
had sweet honey inside.

"In these combs," the queen said,

"we store honey away."

"This is fun!" Sally cried.

"I could do this all day."

48

"Next, we must cover
the combs," said the queen.
"This protects the honey
and helps keep it clean."
"I like honey," said Nick.
"I like honey a lot.
But making it is much
more work than I thought!"

"It's late," said the Cat,

"and it's time we must go,

but we'll come back to visit

you all soon, I know."

"So long!" buzzed the bees.

"And be sure to come back

anytime you want honey

to eat for a snack."

Back home they all opened
their gifts from the queen—
more jars of honey than
they'd ever seen!
"The note says," said Sally,
"'We want to give you
the world's sweetest honey,
from the Hive of Buzzoo.'"

"I liked meeting the queen
and flying through trees.
But what I liked most,"
Nick said . . .

"... was dancing with bees!"

Step This Way

by Tish Rabe
from a script by Graham Ralph
illustrated by Tom Brannon

Random House 🏠 New York

"These shoes are cool," said Nick.
"But as you can see,
    they may fit your dad
    but they're too big for me."

"When I wear my mom's shoes,"
said Sally, "I fall.
Her shoes are too big
and my feet are too small."

"Shoe trouble?" the Cat said.

"Well, I have some news.

Not everyone's feet can

fit in the same shoes.

"Feet come in all sizes,
    and soon you'll see that
    some are flippy, some flappy,
    and some feet are flat.

"Want to see some neat feet?
Well, today I'll take you
to a faraway place:
Bing-Bungle-Ba-Boo!
It's a wonderful place
full of friends you will meet.
And each of them has,
oh, such different feet!"

In minutes they landed
in Bing-Bungle-Ba-Boo,
right by a lake,
and the Cat called, "Yoo-hoo!"

"Hello there, Cat! Welcome
  to my lake," said a duck.
"Emily!" cried the Cat.
"There you are! We're in luck!

"Meet Emily, one of
my friends," said the Cat.
"As you see, her two feet
are all flippy and flat."

"It's true," said the duck.
"My feet are long and wide.
Let's swim and I'll race you
to the other side."

The kids tried their best,
but soon Sally said,
"We've fallen behind.
Emily's way ahead!"

"She won," said the Cat,
"and we came in last.
Her feet push the water
so she can swim fast.

"Duck feet are perfect
for swimming, it's true.
With my Flipper-ma-zippers
we can swim fast, too."

They swam really fast
and crossed the finish line.
Then they heard a voice call,
"Do you have feet like mine?"

"Nick and Sally," the Cat said,

"I'd like you to meet

Mikey the Lemur,

who hangs by his feet."

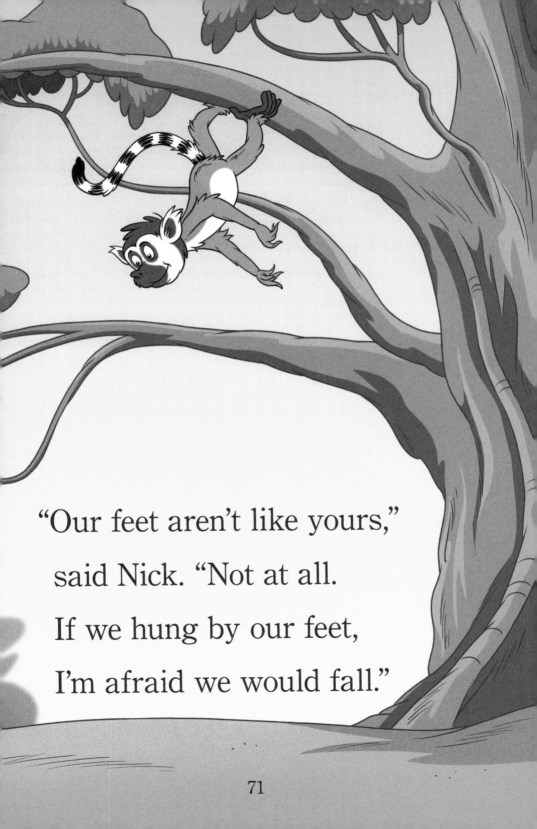

"Our feet aren't like yours,"
said Nick. "Not at all.
If we hung by our feet,
I'm afraid we would fall."

"I have lemur feet,"
said the Cat, "just for you.
Now you can hang
the way Mikey can do."

Before the kids knew it,
they were up in a tree.
"I can hang like a lemur,"
said Nick. "Look at me!"

"Try this!" Mikey said.

"You will think that it's neat.

You can hang upside down

just by using your feet."

"Lemurs are great climbers,"
a voice said, "but see?
Nobody is better
at climbing than me!"

"Greg the Gecko!" the Cat said.
"We're glad to see you.
Geckos have feet
that can stick just like glue."

"Tiny hairs," said Greg,
"help my feet to grip.
These hairs let me hold on
so I do not slip."

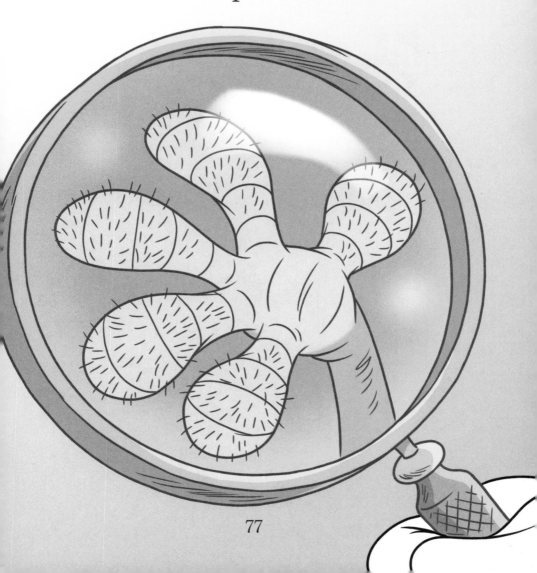

77

The Cat passed out gecko feet.

Nick said, "This is tricky.

I can't move at all.

My feet are too sticky."

"Look!" said the gecko.

"I'll show you my trick—
    press and peel, peel and press,
    and your feet will not stick."

They pressed and they peeled,
and the gecko was right.
They walked upside down,
and their feet held on tight.

"I can walk like a gecko!"
said Nick. "Who would guess
you can walk upside down
if you peel and you press?

"Try duck feet for swimming,
and lemurs' for gripping.
The feet of a gecko
will keep you from slipping.

"But, Sally, I think that
when we get back home,
I'll return your dad's shoes
and just wear . . .

"... my own!"

The Tree Doctor

by Tish Rabe

from a script by Bernice Vanderlaan

illustrated by Tom Brannon

Random House 🏠 New York

"Breakfast!" called Sally.

"The pancakes are hot!
  Let's find out how much
  maple syrup we've got."

"Trees give sap to make syrup,"
  said Nick, "but this one
  is so small, we can't make
  any syrup. No fun!"

"I smell pancakes!" the Cat cried.

"Oh, I hope I am right.

I love golden pancakes,

all fluffy and light,

with sweet maple syrup.

Oh, pour me some, please!
It's my favorite thing
that we get from the trees."

"We've got pancakes," said Nick.
"But unfortunately,
no sap to make syrup
from our maple tree."

"Not to worry!" the Cat said.

"Today I'll take you

to meet the Tree Doctor.

He'll know what to do."

"Meet Dr. Twiggles!

He takes care of trees.

He swings through the branches

and hangs by his knees!"

"Hello," said the doctor.
"Yes, it's up to me
to respond to and treat
every tree-mergency!"

Dr. Twigberry Twiggles
2 Spruce Street
Wild Woolly Wood

If your pine is in pain or your oak's not OK,
call me night or day. I'll be there right away.

"Now, what brings you three
to the Wild Woolly Wood?"
"Our tree's not growing,"
answered Nick, "as it should."

94

"Little tree," said the doctor,

"how are you feeling?

Are your twigs in a twist?

Has your bark started peeling?"

"Hmm . . . color's nice and dark.

Stem is not bumpy.

Branches aren't brittle.

Twigs are not lumpy.

But these leaves are drooping,

and that means, I'd say,

I should check your tree's roots

and do so right away."

96

"Check the roots?" Sally asked.

"How can you do that?"

"To the Thinga-ma-jigger!"

cried the Cat in the Hat.

"Flip the Thrilla-ma-driller
and we'll see if it's ill.
If you've never seen tree roots,
well, soon we all will!"

"Look at that," said Nick.

"This really is neat.

The roots of a tree

are like a tree's feet."

"AbsoROOTly!" the Cat cried.
"I happen to know
    roots soak up food and water
    and help a tree grow."

"I've got it!" the doc said.

"Now I see why
your tree isn't growing.
The soil is too dry."

"It needs water?" the Cat asked.

"I know what to do.
This is a job
for Thing One and Thing Two!"

Those two Things jumped out,
and they gave a big yank
to the crank on the side
of the Thinga-ma-tank.

But they turned it too far
and they turned it too fast.
Water shot out in a
soaking-wet blast!

"Good job!" said the doc.
"But our work is not done.
    To get healthy, your tree
    needs to get lots of sun."
"I know!" cried the Cat.
"Your tree will feel right
    when my Brighta-ma-lighter
    gives it sunlight."

"Now just wait," said the doc.
"In forty years you can tap
your tree and make syrup
from the maple tree sap."

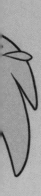

"Forty years!" said Nick.
"When our tree is that old,
our stack of pancakes
will REALLY be cold!"

"No problem!" said the doc.
"For I have right here
some syrup I made
in the spring of last year.

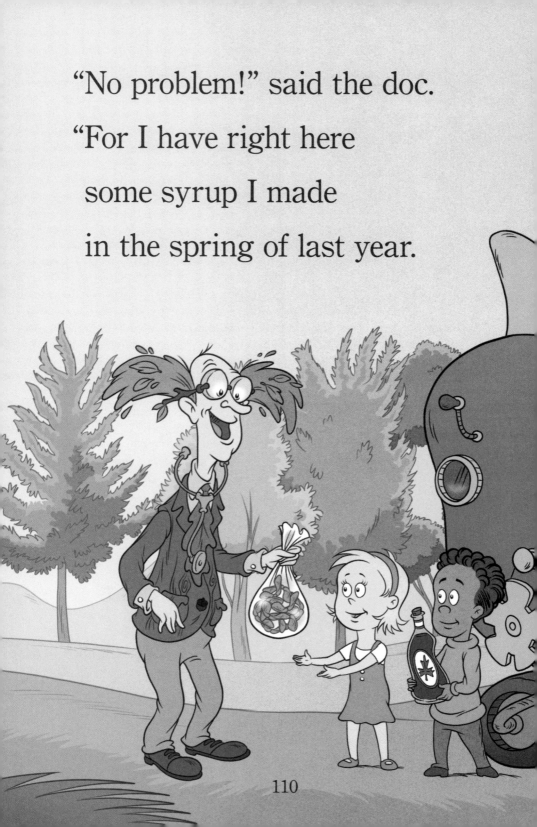

And I have something else—
a bag of maple keys,
full of maple tree seeds
to grow even more trees."

Back home, Nick said,
"This syrup is good
   and I had lots of fun
   in the Wild Woolly Wood."
"Eat up!" said the Cat.
"Then I need your help, please.
   After breakfast let's go
   and plant . . .

"... more maple trees!"

Now You See Me...

by Tish Rabe

from a television script
by Katherine Standford

illustrated by Christopher Moroney

Random House 🏠 New York

Nick said, "It's vacation!
And we have all week
to play games and have fun.
Want to play hide-and-seek?"

"You count and I'll hide,"
Sally said. "And you'll see—
I'll hide so well that
you'll never find me!"

Sally looked till she found
a good hiding spot.
". . . Ten!" Nick called out.
"Coming! Ready or not!"

Where was Sally hiding?
In less than a minute,
Nick ran to the wheelbarrow
and found Sally in it!

"Hide-and-seek!" cried the Cat.
"Oh, I'm so glad I came!
The counting! The hiding!
It's my favorite game!"
"It's great!" Nick agreed.
Sally said as she sighed,
"But Nick always finds me
wherever I hide."

121

"Aha!" said the Cat.
"We must leave right away
to meet my friend Gecko,
who plays every day.

122

He hides in the day
and also at night.
It helps him stay safe
to keep out of sight."

124

So they flew to the jungle.

It was steamy and hot.

"My friend," said the Cat,

"is not easy to spot.

Cam-ou-flage helps him hide.

It is his hiding trick."

"Cam-ou-*what*? I don't know

what that word means!" said Nick.

"I'll explain," said the Cat.
"Camouflage is the way
some animals stay
out of sight every day.

Camouflage helps them hide
so they will not be found.
It helps them blend in
with whatever's around."

"That Gecko blends in.

He's not easy to see."

"Hello!" Gecko called.

"Are you looking for me?

My tail looks leaf-like

and my skin is light brown.

I'm hanging right here in

this tree upside down!"

130

"Could you show us," asked Sally,
"how to hide like you do?
We want to learn how
to use camouflage too!"
"In the jungle," said Gecko,
"your clothes are too bright.
You need to blend in
so you stay out of sight."

"We can't hide dressed like this,"
said Nick. "What to do?"
"You need help," said the Cat,
"from Thing One and Thing Two!"
"Can you help us," asked Sally,
"look leafy and green?
If we look like the jungle,
we'll never be seen."

So, before the kids knew it,
they got a surprise—
Things One and Two made
them the perfect disguise!

"Mr. Gecko," said Nick,

"you can hide, it is true.

But can you find us

when we're hiding from *you*?"

135

"Of course!" Gecko said, but when he looked around, those camouflaged kids were nowhere to be found!

He looked in the shadows
and looked in the light.
They were hiding so well
they were nowhere in sight.

Then all of a sudden
a tree started to wiggle.
"Wait!" Gecko said.
"I just heard someone giggle!
Out here in the jungle,"
he said with a smile,
"the trees haven't giggled
in quite a long while."

"Nick," Sally asked,
"when I was hiding today,
how did you find where
I was right away?"
"Well," Nick said, "finding
you wasn't hard.
Your dress was the only pink
thing in my yard."

"Hide-and-seek," said the Cat,
"is so much fun to play.
I could play it with Gecko
and you every day.

But we have to go now.

We'll be back soon, I know.

Goodbye, Gecko!

Oh . . . Gecko?

"NOW where did he go?"

Hooray for Hair!

by Tish Rabe

from a script by Karen Moonah

illustrated by Tom Brannon

Random House 🏠 New York

"Crazy Hair Day in school
is tomorrow," said Nick.
"We need crazy hair
and we both need it quick.
Short on the top?
Or long on each side?
Straight, wavy, or curly?
I just can't decide."

"Did you say crazy hair?"
said the Cat. "Jump in back.
Today I will take you
to visit a yak.
His hair is yak-tastic.
It's shaggy and thick."
"Sounds like a really cool
hairstyle," said Nick.

"Welcome to Hilly Hazair,"
said the yak.
"It's been a long time
and I'm glad you are back."

"You have nice hair,

Mister Yak," Sally said.

"I wish I had hair

just like yours on my head."

"Please," said the yak,
"just call me Yancy.
My hair is shaggy,
but not very fancy."

"If it's yak hair you want,"
said the Cat, "I'll show you
just what my new
Wig-o-lator can do!

"It springs and it sings,
and in just a short while,
it will give both of you
a super hairstyle.

"You'll love your new look!"
The Cat lowered the hood.
"Oh boy!" whispered Nick.
"This is gonna be good."

The Cat pushed a button
and the thing started dinging.
Buzzers were buzzing.
Bells began ringing.

"It tickles!" said Nick.

"This is fun!" Sally said.

"It is putting a wig
on the top of my head."

In less than a minute
both Sally and Nick
had hair like a yak's.
It was shaggy and thick.
"You look great!" said Yancy.
"It's easy to see,
with your thick, shaggy hair,
you two look just like me."

"It's cold here in

Hilly Hazair," Sally said.

"The only thing warm

is the top of my head.

It's fun to have thick hair

like Yancy has got,

but in summer this thick hair

would really be hot."

161

"Then you'd need hair
of a much different sort.
Like my friend," said the Cat,
"who has hair that is short.

"I will take you
to Blue-Puddle-a-Roo
to meet Celia the Seal.
She can't wait to meet you."

"Hey, Cat!" cried Celia.

"I've been waiting all week."

"Celia," said the Cat,

"has short hair that is sleek."

"Jump in, kids," said Celia.

"The water is fine.

If you're a fur seal,

you need short hair like mine."

"The water's so cold,"
said Sally. "How do you
swim all day long
in Blue-Puddle-a-Roo?"

"I've two layers of hair,"
Celia said. "This is why
though the top one gets wet,
my skin still stays dry.

"I just go jump in
the water, and poof!
I'm warm because
my hair's waterproof."

Seal

Yak

Porcupine

170

"On my Wig-o-lator,"
the Cat said, "this wheel
will spin to give you
the hair of a seal!"

"It feels good," said Sally.
"But I just don't know
if yak hair or seal hair
is how we should go.

"Long hair is warmer,

   but short hair is neat."

"Come on!" said the Cat.

"There's one more friend to meet.

"Here in Poki Moloki

lives a good friend of mine.

His name is Quincy.

He's a fine porcupine.

Quincy has talent.

He's really the best.

He can fluff up his quills

in a porcupine crest."

175

"Hello, Cat," said Quincy.

"Be careful. Stand back!

My sharp quills protect me

from any attack.

My quills are like hair,

but they're sharp to the touch.

Do you have quills, Nick?"

Nick said, "No, not so much."

"To the Wig-o-lator!" the Cat cried.

"Don't run! Get in line.

And you'll soon have quills

like a fine porcupine.

This is a hairstyle

that everyone likes.

Soon you will each have . . .

". . . a head full of spikes!"

"We look pretty sharp,"
   Sally said with a smile.
"But I'm not sure that
   porcupine quills are our style."

"It's time to head back,"
said the Cat. "So let's fly!"
"See you later!" said Quincy.
The kids called, "Goodbye!"

"Cat," Sally said,
"before we went to Hazair,
I'd never seen so many
new kinds of hair.
Hair keeps yaks warm
and keeps a seal dry.
Quills protect Quincy,
who's such a nice guy."

"You're right," said the Cat.
"Hair is not just for show.
It can help you stay warm
in the cold winter snow.
It keeps porcupines
from becoming a meal
and helps keep you dry
if you are a fur seal."

"For Crazy Hair Day," said Nick,
"what we'll do
   is have yak hair and seal hair
   and porcupine, too!

186

"Crazy Hair Day is
going to be great.
Let's both get up early
so we won't be late."

"How was Crazy Hair Day
today?" asked the Cat.
"I wore," said Nick,
"a yak-seal-porcupine hat.
Having yak-seal-porcupine
hair wasn't bad,
but now I'll go back
to the hair . . .

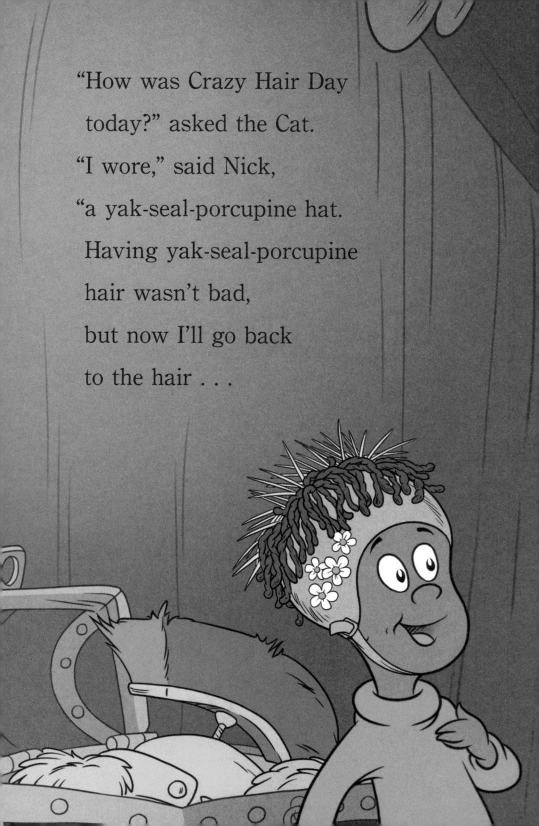

"... that I had!"